An ECS **Once Upon A Time**™ Book, Grades K-2

Chicken Licken

Critical Thinking and Writing Activities
For the Emerging Reader

Arlene Capriola and Rigmor Swensen
Illustrated by Kathy Burns

Welcome to the Once Upon A Time™ series!

Learning to read should be fun! Children focus longer and retain more when they are doing activities they enjoy. The 10-book **Once Upon A Time**™ series teaches reading and writing as a fun, engaging process. Children create their own storybooks (complete with illustrations!) by elaborating on well-known fairy tales. Familiar story lines and colorful characters will amuse and entertain children for hours as they improve reading and writing skills.

The **Once Upon A Time**™ series is more than just fun. It is an effective means of advancing reading and writing levels. Educators agree that emerging readers should begin reading with materials that provide higher-level thinking skills and practice in following directions. Research emphasizes that reading and writing should begin simultaneously. The **Once Upon A Time**™ series provides these elements in a format attractive to children. Each book in the series encourages:

- Reading beyond the blank before answering, learning to use context clues
- Rereading each completed chapter, asking, "Does your story make sense?"
- Referring to the story for clues to answer TELL and GUESS questions
- Becoming involved in the story and risk-taking
- Reading directions carefully prior to drawing comprehension pictures
- Using complete sentences for all writing activities

Welcome to the fairy-tale world of learning with the **Once Upon A Time**™ series! Have fun!

About the Authors...

Arlene Capriola, an elementary reading specialist, holds a combined master's degree in reading and learning disabilities. She has three sons and resides with her husband, John, in Long Island, New York.

Rigmor Swensen is a freelance writer and former teacher of secondary reading and English literature. She holds a master's degree in reading and special education. Riggie, mother of three, lives in Long Island, New York, with her husband, Roy. She and Arlene have enjoyed collaborating on several reading workbook series.

 The Once Upon A Time™ series is also available on audio tapes!

To order, contact your local school supply store or –

ECS Learning Systems, Inc.
P.O. Box 791437
San Antonio, Texas 78279-1437

Editor: Cherisse Mastry
Cover/Page Layout & Graphics: Kirstin Simpson
Book Design: Educational Media Services

ISBN 1-57022-139-1

©1998 by ECS Learning Systems, Inc., San Antonio, Texas. All rights reserved. No part of this publication may be reproduced, stored in a retrieval system, or transmitted in any way or by any means (electronic, mechanical, photocopying, recording, or otherwise) without prior written permission from ECS Learning Systems, Inc., with the exceptions found below.

Photocopying of student worksheets by a teacher who purchased this publication for his/her own class is permissible. Reproduction of any part of this publication for an entire school or for a school system or for commercial sale is strictly prohibited. **Copyright infringement is a violation of Federal Law.**

Printed in the United States of America.

My Play about...

(Draw your own cover.)

Chicken Licken

by

_____

(Write your name.)

Cast of Characters

 Author

 Chicken Licken

 Henny Penny

 Goosey Loosey

 Ducky Lucky

 Turkey Lurkey

 Foxy Loxy

Chapter 1

 Chicken Licken got up with the sun.

She went _____ into the barnyard.
(by, out)

It was a fine summer day.

The grass was _____.
(green, toad)

The sky was blue.

Chicken Licken went to the big oak tree.

She began to dig _____ her feet.
(then, with)

She got a fat, brown worm.

It was a _____ way to start.
(good, red)

She dug with her beak.

She got _____ seeds.
(what, some)

They were good to eat.

Tell: What time of day was it?

It was _____

Make the Picture

Chicken Licken is in the barnyard.

- **Draw** the grass, the sky, and the worm.
- Make them the colors in the story.

Chapter 2

Chicken Licken sat _____ the oak tree.
(under, to)

Just then, a big brown acorn fell.

It hit Chicken Licken on top of her head.

Oh! My head! _____ head!
(So, My)

There is _____ big bump on it!
(a, cat)

Chicken Licken looked this way.

She looked that way.

She did not see the big _____ acorn.
(frog, brown)

What is going on?

Oh, no! The sky is falling!

What _____ I do?
(are, can)

Guess: What will Chicken Licken do?

Chicken Licken will _____

_____

1	2	3

Make the Picture
Where is Chicken Licken?

- In box **1** make a big brown tree.
- In box **3** make 3 more acorns and the sun.
- In box **2** make green grass by the acorn.

Chapter 3

The sky is falling.

I must go _____ the king.
(top, tell)

Chicken Licken ran to the hen house.

The sand flew this _____ and that.
(way, round)

Henny Penny was sitting on her nest.

Come with me! Come _____ me!
(or, with)

Where are we going, Chicken Licken?

I was just digging _____ the sand.
(in, say)

I _____ a worm and some seeds.
(top, got)

Then the sky fell on me.

We must go tell the king.

Guess: Will Henny Penny go with her?

Henny Penny _____

_____

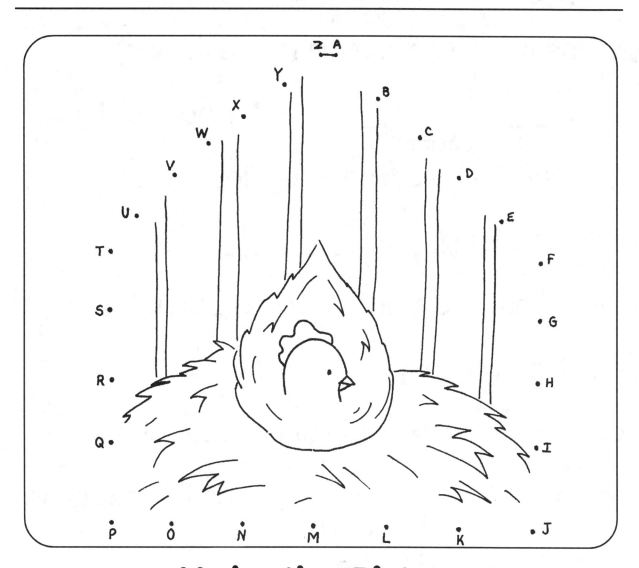

Make the Picture

Henny Penny is sitting on her nest.
Where is her nest?

- Go dot-to-dot to see.
- **Color** the picture.

Chapter 4

I will help you, Chicken Licken.

Let us go as _____ as we can.
(fast, little)

So the two friends set off to see the king.

They_____ to the barnyard gate.
(tap, ran)

Goosey Loosey sat on the gate.

Come with us! _____ with us!
(Come, Swim)

Where are you going, Chicken Licken

and Henny Penny?

Chicken Licken was digging in the sand.

She got a _____ and some seeds.
(fish, worm)

Then the sky fell on her.

We must go tell the _____ .
(dad, king)

Tell: Are the friends in a rush?

_____ . I can tell because Henny Penny
(Yes, No)

says _____

Make the Picture

Here is Goosey Loosey.

- Make a red gate for her to swing on.
- Put 5 yellow flowers by the gate.
- Make a big tree, too.

Chapter 5

I will help you, Chicken Licken.

Let us go as fast as we _____.
(can, be)

The three friends set off to see the king.

They got as _____ as the blue pond.
(happy, far)

Ducky Lucky was having his morning swim.

Come with us! Come with _____.
(game, us)

Where are you going, Chicken Licken, Henny Penny, and Goosey Loosey?

We are _____ to see the king.
(taking, going)

Chicken Licken was digging in the sand.

She got a worm and some seeds.

Then the _____ fell on her.
(hay, sky)

We must go tell the king.

Tell: How many friends are going now?

Now there are _____

_____

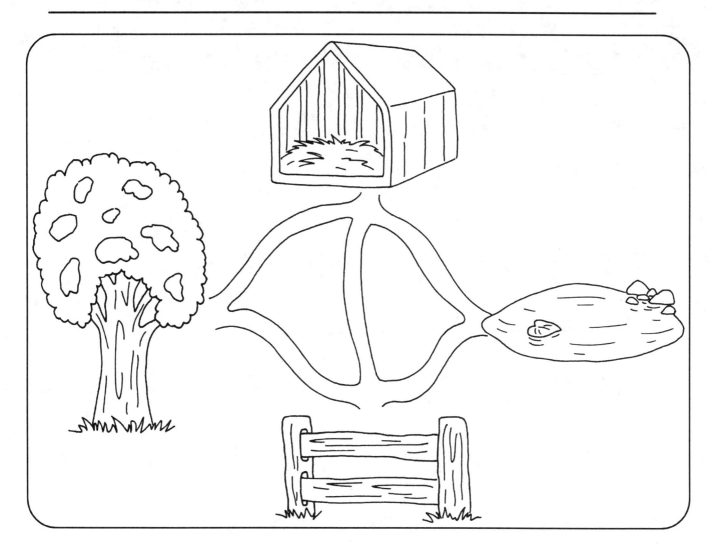

Make the Picture

Chicken Licken went to many places.

- Put a 1 on the spot where she was **first**.
- Then put 2, 3, 4 to show where she went **next**.

Chapter 6

I will help _____ , Chicken Licken.
(you, the)

Let _____ go as fast as we can.
(us, can)

So the four friends set off to see the king.

They saw Turkey Lurkey in the grass.

Come with us! Come with _____ !
(us, they)

Where are you going, Chicken Licken,

Henny Penny, Goosey Loosey, and

Ducky Lucky?

We are _____ to see the king.
(taking, going)

Chicken Licken was digging in the sand.

She got a worm and some seeds.

Then the sky _____ on her.
(bet, fell)

We must go tell the king.

Guess: What do they think the king will do?

They think the king will _____

_____

Make the Picture
Where was Turkey Lurkey resting?

- Put a ⬭ on the picture that shows it.
- **Color** Turkey Lurkey brown and red.

Chapter 7

I will help you, Chicken Licken.

_____ us go as fast as we can.
      (Let, Trip)

So the five friends set off to see the king.

They had to tell him the sky was falling.

Chicken Licken, Henny Penny, Goosey Loosey,

Ducky Lucky, and Turkey Lurkey

went _____ the path.
         (down, left)

The king must see this _____ bump.
             (small, big)

The king will _____ the sky from falling.
      (sing, stop)

We must go to _____ big house.
        (his, those)

But where is the king's house?

The friends all stopped....

Guess: Do they know where the king's house is?

I think they _____

_____

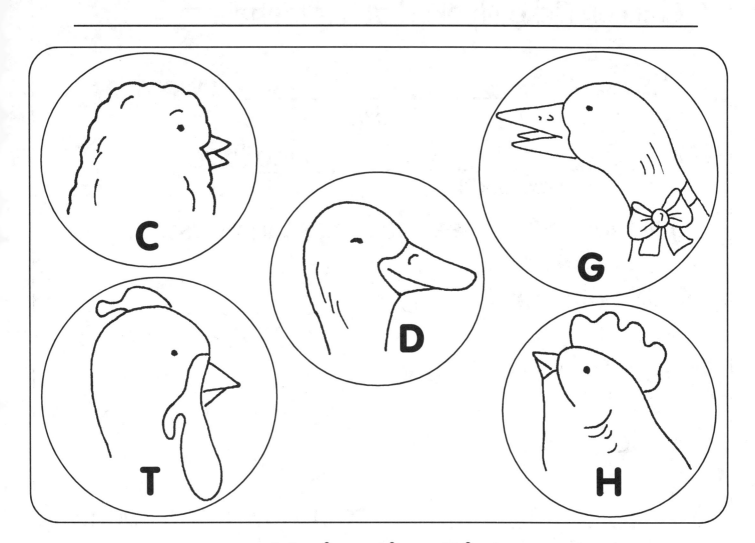

Make the Picture
Who am I? **Write** the letter.

_____ I like the tall grass.   _____ The sky fell on me.

_____ I was in the pond.   _____ I was in my hen house.

_____ I was sitting on a fence.

Chapter 8

They all looked _____ Chicken Licken.
(at, out)

Chicken Licken looked at her friends.

She did not _____ a word.
(eat, say)

It _____ getting late.
(was, does)

Still they did not see the king's big house.

I did not think it was this _____ .
(far, out)

I must have a cold drink.

My feet hurt.

I _____ we come to a pond soon.
(can, hope)

Let us sit down a bit.

We cannot rest.

We must go find the king!

Tell: How do Chicken Licken's friends feel now?

Her friends feel _____

_____

Make the Picture

The five friends cannot find the king's house.
Help them.

• Go the A-B-C way.

Chapter 9

All at once, a red fox came out of the woods.

He had long white teeth.

And he licked his _____ .
(lips, sky)

Hello, friends. My name is Foxy Loxy.

What are you doing in the woods today?

We are going to see the _____ .
(train, king)

Yes, we _____ tell him the sky is falling.
(must, soon)

Chicken Licken was digging in the sand.

She got a _____ and some seeds.
(star, worm)

Then the sky fell on her.

We must go _____ the king.
(sing, tell)

But we cannot **find** the king.

Guess: Is Foxy Loxy a friend?

_____ , Foxy Loxy _____
(Yes, No)

_____

Make the Picture

Foxy Loxy and the others are in the woods.

- Find Foxy Loxy and **color** him red.
- Find the five friends and **color** them.

Chapter 10

The fox looked _____ the five friends.
(of, at)

Then he looked at his thin, thin belly.

I _____ help you find the king.
(cook, can)

I know where he lives.

His house is on _____ of a hill.
(pan, top)

But this is not the path to the king's house.

The path is in the woods.

It goes by _____ den.
(my, red)

I will show you the _____ .
(kind, way)

The five friends looked at Foxy Loxy.

Then they said….

Guess: Will they go with Foxy Loxy?

The five friends will _____

_____

Make the Picture
Color this to tell the five friends what to do.

1 = red   3 = blue
2 = green   4 = yellow

Chapter 11

All Yes, Foxy Loxy, we will come with you.

So they _____ went into the woods.
(all, any)

Soon they were at the fox's _____ .
(cap, den)

Come in _____ to find the way.
(here, by)

It is dark, so come one _____ a time.
(at, and)

I'll be one.

I'll be two.

I'll be three.

I'll be four.

And I'll be five.

They all went into the _____ dark den.
(bird's, fox's)

And no one told the king the sky was falling.

Tell: What did the fox do with the five friends?

Foxy Loxy _____

_____

Make the Picture

What did the five friends say?

• **Write** the words that are missing.

Instant Recap

Here is the story of Chicken Licken again.
Write the words to tell the story.
The word box will help you.

Chicken Licken got up with the sun. She went to the

big oak tree to dig. She got a big fat worm and some

_____ . Just then, a big brown

acorn fell on her head. She said, **"Oh, no! The sky is**

falling!" She ran to tell the _____ .

On the way Chicken Licken met Henny Penny and

Goosey Loosey and Ducky Lucky and Turkey Lurkey.

She told them that the sky was _____ .

They said, "We must go tell the king!" So they went with

Chicken Licken to _____ the king.

The five friends got lost. They did not know the way to the king's _____ . All at once, a red fox came out of the woods. The five friends told him the _____ was falling. Foxy Loxy said, "I can help you find the king. _____ with me."

So _____ did. Foxy Loxy led them into the woods. He _____ them to his den. Then he _____ them all.

The End

| they | ate | seeds | house | tell |
| king | led | sky | falling | Come |

Missing Chicken!

Name: _____

Color: _____

Has a _____ on her head.

Likes to eat _____ and _____.

Last seen digging under _____

Said she was on her way to _____
_____

If you see Chicken Licken, tell her that

_____ is looking for her.
(Write your name.)

Has anyone seen Chicken Licken?
Fill in this "Missing Chicken" sign.
Draw her picture.
Then put this up for all to see.

Playwright's Page

You are the playwright.
Draw your picture in the box below.

1. **Read** your play to five others.

2. **Tell** them to put their names below.

3. Let them **tell** you how they like your play.

4. Let them **tell** you how they like your pictures.

_____
(Write your name.)